JN078627

企画・編集／イントロデュース宮崎
英文アドバイス／ Alice Holmes

鉱脈社

Prologue

Miyazaki is said to be a region of mythology and legend.

The purpose of the publication of this book is to introduce the reader to Miyazaki's myths and folktales through English, so non-Japanese people may also learn about them, and understand the cultural and historical background of the Miyazaki region.

First, "Prince Ninigi and Princess Konohanasakuya" tells the story of the encounter between a young man and woman, and is from Kojiki and Nihon Shoki.

Kojiki and Nihon Shoki were respectively written by the Japanese authorities in A.D.700s, which tell the birth and beginning of Japan and its history.

Next, is the story of "Umisachihiko and Yamasachihiko" which also originated in mythology. They are the children of Prince Ninigi and Princess Konohanasakuya. Every Japanese knows the story well since childhood.

Then "Gyoran Kannon", a folktale handed down in the Aoki District of Miyazaki, is featured. This is an interesting story of the Gyoran Kannon that is still housed in a temple in the area to this day.

The folktale "The Story of Okuragahama" is also well-known in Miyazaki. In present day Hyuga City in Miyazaki Prefecture, there are beaches called Okuragahama and Okanegahama. Okuragahama is well known for abundant and supreme clam harvests.

Next, is the folktale "Kagekiyo and his Daughter Hitomaru." The main stage of this story is Shimokitakata Town of Miyazaki City today, and here the legend of Ikime Shrine is told.

The last story is "The Chapped Boy", which is an interesting folktale set in Mt.Sobo and Takachiho District.

We hope that junior high and high school students in Miyazaki will be interested in the myths and folktales through English study.

Readers can also listen to the audio version of the stories in English.

はじめに

宮崎は神話と伝説の地といわれています。

この本の発行の目的は、英語を通して宮崎の神話や民話等を読者に紹介(しょうかい)することにあり、外国の人々もまた、宮崎の神話・民話を知ることにより、宮崎地方の文化的・歴史的な背景を理解していただけるでしょう。

まず、「ニニギノミコトとコノハナサクヤヒメ」が、若い男女の出会いの物語として語られます。出典は古事記と日本書紀です。

古事記および日本書紀は、西暦(せいれき)700年代に、当時の権威者が、日本の誕生と生い立ち及びその歴史を書いたものです。

次にニニギノミコトとコノハナサクヤヒメの子どもである「海幸彦(うみさちひこ)と山幸彦(やまさちひこ)」の神話に基づいた物語であり、日本人は誰(だれ)でも、子どもの頃からよく知っています。

続いては「魚籃(ぎょらん)観音」という宮崎市の檍(あおき)地区に伝承されている民話です。なかなか面白い話で、その観音様は、現在でもこの地区のお寺に収蔵されています。

「お倉(くら)ヶ浜(はま)物語」という民話も宮崎ではよく知られています。

現在の宮崎県日向市には、お倉ヶ浜とお金ヶ浜という浜辺があり、お倉ヶ浜はたくさんの品質の良い蛤(はまぐり)がよく採れることで有名です。

次に「景清(かげきよ)とその娘人丸(むすめひとまる)」という民話は、現在の宮崎市の下北方町が主な舞台(ぶたい)で、ここで生目神社の伝説も語られます。

最後の民話は、「あかぎれ少年」というもので、祖母山と高千穂(たかちほ)地方における面白い一つの民話です。

宮崎の中高生等が、英語を通して、神話・民話に興味を持つことを期待しています。

読者は、付録のCDで英文を聞くこともできます。

CONTENTS

CDについて

CDには本書に収録されたお話の英文音読がすべて収録されています。お手本にしながら音読の練習をしてみましょう。

★トラック番号は Track #01 のようにそれぞれの英文の最初に示されています。

■ナレーション　Alice Holmes

Mythology and Folktales in Miyazaki

英語で楽しむ宮崎の神話と民話

Track #01

Prince Ninigi and Princess Konohanasakuya

ニニギノミコトとコノハナサクヤヒメ

This is a legend concerning the Birth of Japan based on Japanese Mythology. The hero and heroine are a young man and woman.

Long long ago there were many Gods in Takamagahara, a place not on land but high in the sky far above the clouds. You might say that the concept is similar to 'Heaven' in the West.

In Japanese, the 'taka' of Takamagahara means 'high' and the 'hara' means 'field'.

The most supreme of the gods, Goddess Amaterasu,lived there. She was known as the goddess of the sun.

Amaterasu sent other gods to govern the earth world below, which had been in turmoil. As a result, the disturbance below eventually subsided, and it became peaceful.

Amaterasu decided to dispatch her grandson, Prince Ninigi to stabilize and govern the ground on the earth world below for eternity. Amaterasu ordered Prince Ninigi, "You must rule Toyoashiharamizuho Country. Go down to the earth world immediately."

In Japanese mythology, Toyoashiharamizuho Country meant 'the country where thick reeds overgrow and golden ears of rice spread'.

When Prince Ninigi tried to descend, another god appeared in the distance. This god was radiating light from his body.

Amaterasu called the god Amenouzume and ordered, "You are a woman but a strong-minded god. Go and ask who is that god standing over there." So Amenouzume went there and asked. The strange god replied, "I am the god Sarutahiko, I heard that the son of the most noble god will go down to the earth, so I came here to guide him."

Before departure, Amaterasu called Prince Ninigi, and gave him the *Yasaka* comma-shaped bead and the mirror, and the *Kusanagi* sword. These are three kinds of sacred treasures, representing the throne of the Emperor. "You should think of this mirror as my soul and serve it as if serving the real me," Amaterasu said.

Finally it was time to leave. Prince Ninigi started to leave from Takamagahara with his companions. He majestically parted the overlapping clouds, opened a path, and proceeded towards the earth below. At last Prince Ninigi descended to arrive at Mt. Futakami of the Takachiho District in Himuka which was located in the Tsukushi region in Kyushu, Japan.

The place where Ninigi descended is said to be present-day Takachiho Town in Miyazaki Prefecture and Mt. Futakami is also located there.

However, some people say the place Prince Ninigi descended is not Takachiho Town, but is in fact Mt. Takachiho of the southwest Kirishima mountain range, located 100 kilometres away from Takachiho Town. Mt.Takachiho is a 1,574 meter high mountain on the borders of today's Miyazaki Prefecture and Kagoshima Prefecture.

There are some other people who say that it is not important to detect the exact point of descent, as we only need to know the place was in Southern Kyushu in Japan, because it is not the real world but rather a legend and myth. Therefore, to this day, the dispute has not been settled.

Prince Ninigi descended to the earth below and exclaimed, "This is a good place! The morning sun is thrusting straight and the sunset shines so beautifully, how wonderful this land is." He then went on to build a large, very high palace there.

One day Prince Ninigi, at the Cape of Kasasa, happened to meet with Princess Konohanasakuya, daughter of the god Ooyamatsumi. Prince Ninigi was so struck by Princess Konohanasakuya's beauty that he asked her father for permission to marry her.

Princess Konohanasakuya's father, the god Ooyamatsumi allowed it under the condition of also marrying her older sister Princess Iwanaga. However, Prince Ninigi refused this condition, and married only Princess Konohana while sending Princess Iwanaga back to her father, because her appearance was hard to look at.

The god Ooyamatsumi said, "The husband of Princess Konohanasakuya can prosper with beauty like flowers do, but Princess Iwanaga's husband can endure windstorms and have eternal life."

For that reason, Prince Ninigi was destined to have only a mortal life.

Prince Ninigi and Princess Konohanasakuya lived together for only one night, for the next day Ninigi had to go and fight for the building of the country while leaving his wife behind.

After some time had passed, Prince Ninigi returned to Princess Konohanasakuya and she told him that she was pregnant. Prince Ninigi was surprised and said. "I can't believe that you are pregnant, because we only spent one day together." So the princess said, "If you say so I will deliver the baby while a fire is ablaze. If the precious baby is indeed yours, then I will give birth to the baby safely."

Princess Konohanasakuya entered the cottage to prepare for childbirth. She closed the entrances, piled dead reeds on the roof, and ordered followers to set it on fire. The fire surrounded the cottage in no time. People prayed for the Princess and a safe birth, while the flames burned furiously, at last the Princess gave birth to triplets while in extreme danger.

It is said that the place where the newborn babies took their first bath with mild warm water was in the Pond of Koyu. This pond is located in Saito City in the Koyu District of Miyazaki Prefecture. In Japanese, the 'ko' of *koyu* means 'child' and the 'yu' means 'hot water'.

The triplets were all three boys. Among the sons, the eldest brother was called Prince Hoderi and the youngest brother was called Prince Hoori.

There is a famous story about these two brothers, in which Prince Hoderi was called Umisachihiko and Prince Hoori was called Yamasachihiko.

Every Japanese person is familiar with this interesting story of Yamasachihiko and Umisachihiko.

日本語訳

ニニギノミコトとコノハナサクヤヒメ

この伝説は、日本の神話に基づいた、日本の誕生にまつわるものです。主人公は、二人の男女の若者です。

むかし、むかし、はるかむかし、地上ではない高天原（たかまがはら）という雲のはるか上の天上界に、多くの神々がいました。この高天原は、西欧（せいおう）の天国と似た概念（がいねん）と考えてよいでしょう。

そこには神様の中では最も尊いアマテラスオオミカミという女神がいました。太陽の神様として知られています。

アマテラスは、乱れていた地上の世界を治めさせるため、他の神々を派遣（はけん）しました。その結果、やがて地上世界も静かになり、平和が訪れました。

アマテラスは、孫であるニニギノミコトを派遣することにして、地上世界を永遠に安定して治めさせることにしました。

アマテラスは、ニニギノミコトにお命じになりました。

「あなたは、トヨアシハラミズホの国を治めなければなりません。地上世界へ一日も早くご出発しなさい」

日本の神話で、トヨアシハラミズホの国とは、葦（あし）がおい茂（しげ）り、稲（いね）が豊かに実る国のことを意味します。

ニニギがお降（お）りなさろうとすると、遠くに別の神様が現れました。この神は体からこうこうと光を放っていました。

アマテラスは、アメノウズメノカミをお呼びになり、「あなたは女性だが気の強い神である。あそこに立っている神は誰なのか行って尋ねてきなさい」とお命じになりました。アメノウズメノカミがそこに行き、尋ねると、「私はサルタヒコノカミと言います。高貴な神の御子が地上にお降りになると聞いて、ご案内のために参上しました」とその見知らぬ神は答えました。

出発前に、アマテラスはニニギをお呼びになり、ヤサカの勾玉および鏡とクサナギの剣をお与えになりました。これらは三種の神器というもので、天皇家の王位を表しています。

「この鏡を私の魂だと思い、本当の私に仕えるようにして仕えなさい」とアマテラスは、おっしゃいました。

いよいよご出発です。ニニギはお供を連れて、高天原を出立しました。堂々として、幾重にも重なる雲を押し分けて、道を開かれ、下の地上に向かって進まれました。ついにニニギは、日本の九州、筑紫地方の日向の高千穂地区の二上岳に降下されました。

ニニギが降りた場所は、現在の宮崎県の高千穂町にあたるといわれ、ここには二上岳もあります。

しかしながら、ニニギの降りた場所は、高千穂町ではなく、ここから南西100kmにある霧島山脈にある高千穂峰であると主張する人々がいます。高千穂峰は、現在の宮崎県と鹿児島県の県境に位置する1,574mの高い山です。

次のように主張する人々もいます。

ニニギが降りた地点を正確に特定することより、その地点を日本の南九州と理解することが大事なことです。なぜなら、これは事実というより、あくまで伝説と神話に基づくものだからです。

このようにして、今日までこの論争には、決着がついていないのです。

地上の国に降りたニニギは、次のように言いました。

「ここはよいところである。朝日がまっすぐさしこみ、夕日が輝くように美しい、素晴らしい土地だ」。そして、次に大きくて大変高い御殿をここにつくりました。

ニニギは、ある日、笠沙の岬で、オオヤマツミノカミの娘コノハナサクヤヒメとお会いになりました。その美しさに心を奪われたニニギは、コノハナサクヤヒメの父に、結婚の許しを請いました。

コノハナサクヤヒメの父であるオオヤマツミノカミは、姉娘のイワナガヒメとともにという条件で許しました。しかしながらニニギはこれに従わずコノハナサクヤヒメだけを妻とされ、イワナガヒメは容姿がきつかったので、父のもとに返しました。

オオヤマツミノカミは、「コノハナサクヤヒメの夫となる人は、花のように美しく栄えることができますが、イワナガヒメの夫は、風雪に耐え、永遠の命を持つことができます」と言いました。

そのため、ニニギは、限りのある命を持つことになってしまいました。

ニニギとコノハナサクヤヒメは、わずか一晩一緒に過ごしたのみで、次の日、ニニギは、コノハナサクヤヒメを残して、国づくりに奔走しなければなりませんでした。

しばらくして、ニニギがコノハナサクヤヒメの元に帰ってきた時、ヒメは懐妊したことを告げました。ニニギは驚き、「あなたと過ごしたのはたった一日なのに、子どもができたとは信じられない」と言いました。

そこでヒメは、「それでは私は、火の燃えさかる中で子を産みましょう。尊い御子の子どもであるならば、無事に生まれるはずです」と言いました。

コノハナサクヤヒメは出産にそなえ産屋に入り、入り口を閉ざし、枯れた葦を屋根に積み、供の者に命じて、火をつけさせました。火はまたたく間に産屋を取り巻きました。人々はこの天を焦がす炎の中、ヒメの安泰と出産の安全を祈りました。ついにヒメは、大変危険な状態で三つ子を産みました。

その赤ちゃんが産湯を使ったところが、児湯の池であるといわれています。この池は現在、宮崎県の児湯地区の西都市にあります。

日本語で児湯の「児」は、子どものことであり、「湯」とは温かい水を意味します。

三人の子どもは、男子でした。

一番上の兄をホデリノミコト、一番下の弟をホオリノミコトと言いました。

この二人の兄弟には有名な物語があり、その中でホデリノミコトは海幸彦、ホオリノミコトは山幸彦と呼ばれています。

日本人なら誰でもこの海幸彦と山幸彦の面白い物語を、知っています。

Track #02

Umisachihiko and Yamasachihiko

海幸彦(うみさちひこ)と山幸彦(やまさちひこ)

Long long ago, a warm tide flowed in the sea, where many fish swam. The sun shone brightly and the mountains were covered with deep greenery. There were many birds and animals.

This is a story of the southern region of Japan, present-day Miyazaki Prefecture on the island of Kyushu. Here two young men lived. Both men were sons of a noble god. The elder brother never failed to catch fish when he went fishing, so he was called Umisachihiko. (*'Umi'* means ocean, *'sachi'* means luck and *'hiko'* is a boy's name in Japanese.) The younger brother ran around the mountains and fields and hunted for bird and animal, so he was called Yamasachihiko.(*'Yama'* means mountain.)

One day Yamasachihiko said, "It is not interesting to do the same things every day, why not exchange our tools?"

The elder brother hesitated, but the younger brother was persistent, so the elder agreed to do so.

So one day, Yamasachihiko borrowed his brother's fishing hook and decided to go to the beach.

He went to the ocean by boat and cast the fishing line into the water, but he could not catch any fish. He previously thought that he would be able to catch as many fish as his brother, which would be great fun. But the fishhook, which brought its owner good luck, lost its magical power when it changed owner. What's more, while fishing, he lost the hook to a big fish.

When Yamasachihiko returned disappointed to the beach, his elder brother had already come back from the mountain and was likewise dissatisfied. After all, the younger brother's bow was also useless if it left its owner's hand.

Drooping his head, the younger brother announced that he had lost the hook while fishing. The elder brother got angry, "That fishhook was precious to me, look for it quickly and return it to me!"

Even if you were told to look for it, there could be no way to find it. The younger brother melted his sword and made a lot of fishhooks from it. He made many as if they spilled out from the palms of both hands.

He offered them to his elder brother. The elder brother rejected them. "I want the fishhook that I lent to you," he said coldly.

The younger brother was at a loss as he stood on the beach. He felt depressed, and didn't know what to do, when someone spoke to him. "Why are you upset?" An old man with a long white beard approached him, but Yamasachihiko didn't know where he came from. Yamasachihiko told him that he was thinking of how to find the fishhook, and he was at a loss for what to do. Then the old man smiled at him and nodded. This old man was a venerable sage named Shiotsuchi who controlled the tides of the sea.

The old man pulled a black comb out of his bag and threw it onto the ground. Then bamboo shoots came out of the ground, grew into big bamboo plants, and became a bamboo forest. The old man cut the bamboo and tightly knitted together a boat made with many pieces of the bamboo. "Take this, a strong tide will lead you to the palace of the god of the sea. There is a spring beside the palace gate, and a big katsura tree with thick branches. If you climb up onto the tree and wait, good things will happen."

Doing exactly what the old man said, Yamasachihiko went onto the boat made of the bamboo. When the boat swayed a bit, it slid offshore as if being pulled by an invisible string.

After a while, a sea fog began to surround the boat and

became gradually thicker, but suddenly it disappeared completely, and a beach was in sight that was covered with beautiful pebbles.

After soaking his feet in the clear water, Yamasachihiko got up onto the beach. It was a strange world filled with a soft milky light. As he passed through the forest, a beautiful palace appeared. A high vermilion-lacquered castle towered above, surrounded by a high fence with a gate.

There was a spring beside the gate, and there was a katsura tree on the bank of the spring. Everything was exactly as the sage Shiotsuchi said. Yamasachihiko did not hesitate to climb up that tree, clinging to one of the thick branches.

How much time had passed? A maid with a bowl came out from inside the gate and approached the spring.

The maid was bent over trying to scoop water from the spring, when she saw the shadow of a young man on the surface of the water. She was surprised and looked up at Yamasachihiko.

Smiling, Yamasachihiko said, “Please let me drink that pure water.”

As he had asked, the maid offered the water. Yamasachihiko didn’t drink it, but took one of the comma-shaped beads (*magatama* in Japanese) that were hung around his neck, held it in his mouth, and then threw it back in the bowl.

The maid was puzzled when she rinsed the bowl.

The magatama Yamasachihiko had spat out was stuck to the bottom. As there was nothing else she could do, she scooped up the water from the spring into the bowl as it was, and took it back to the palace.

At the palace the Princess Toyotama, who was a daughter of the god of the sea, saw the shining magatama stuck to the bottom of the bowl offered by the maid. She felt uneasy.

"Is there anyone outside the gate?" she asked. The maid replied, "there was a splendid young man."

When Princess Toyotama furtively peeped behind the gate, a fine young man was sitting on the branches of the katsura tree, as the maid had said.

The princess' father, the god of the sea, Wadatsumi, heard the news from the princess, "He must be the son of a noble god, so please guide him here carefully," he said, and respectfully gave welcome to Yamasachihiko.

Soon the young couple fell in love and got married.

Every day was novel and fun and Yamasachihiko spent three years in the palace.

However, one day, Yamasachihiko remembered the reason that he had gone there. He had not yet been able to retrieve his brother's hook. When he thought of it, he took a deep breath and sighed. It hurt Princess Toyotama to see her husband feeling bad. "He sighed deeply today, although he had been living happily for three years. I should consult my father," she thought.

"What happened?" Wadatsumi asked Yamasachihiko.

He replied that he was looking for the fishhook of his elder brother that he had lost.

So Wadatsumi, soon gathered all kinds of fish to ask them about the hook, but none of them knew of such a hook. Then a fish remembered and said. "Come to think of it, there was someone who said that the sea bream recently hurt her throat and she was mourning that she couldn't eat food."

So Wadatsumi called the sea bream. When he examined her throat, there was the fishhook that Yamasachihiko had lost. Wadatsumi cleaned the fishhook and gave it to Yamasachihiko. When he got the fishhook which he was looking for, the princess was saddened, knowing that there was no way that she could change Yamasachihiko's mind to leave.

As they parted, Wadatsumi gave detailed instructions to Yamasachihiko.

"When you give this hook back to your brother, you must

turn your back to him and throw it to him, while saying 'painful hook, frustrated hook, poor hook, foolish hook,' and the fishhook will lose its magic power."

"Then, if your elder brother makes a rice field in a high place, you should make one in a low place and if your brother makes it in a low place, make one in a high placc. I am the one who rules the water, so I can make water flow only to your field."

"When your brother goes on a boat to fish, you must stand on shore, make your mouth narrow and breathe out towards the sea."

"Immediately I will make a strong wind and overtake his ship."

"If you do so, in about three years your elder brother will become extremely poor and he may hold a grudge against you and attack you."

"At that time please use these, the Shiomitsu Ball (which means the ball has the power of pulling the tide) and the Shiohi Ball (which means the ball that can push the tide)."

"If you pray for high tide while you hold the Shiomitsu Ball, a high tide will come. For the Shiohi Ball, if you pray that the tide retreat, then the tide will quickly retreat."

Saying this, he gave the two balls to Yamasachihiko.

Now Wadatsumi gathered sharks around him and asked, "The son of a noble god will return to his country on land, how many days will it take for you to carry him?" Each of the sharks responded by estimating the number of days while considering the size of their own body and the strength of their fins, but the Hitohiro Shark said, "If it is me, I will transport him to his own country instantly and report it the same day."(In Japanese *'hitohiro'* means the full breadth between outstretched arms.)

Wadatsumi said, "Then, I will have you carry him there. When you cross the sea, do not let him grow afraid. I forbid it." Finally he granted the Hitohiro Shark the role of transporting Yamasachihiko.

The Hitohiro Shark carried Yamasachihiko to land as quickly as possible, and he met his elder brother Umisachihiko and returned the fishhook. It went without saying that he had followed Wadatsumi's instructions.

Umisachihiko who received the fishhook which had lost its magical power, was not able to catch any fish since regaining the fishhook, and a strong wind blew and overturned his ship.

And when he made a rice field in a high place, a drought continued, and he struggled to obtain water. And when he made a rice field in a low place, rain poured and the field was soaked with water. After three years he became poor.

Suffice to say it was just as the Wadatsumi had said.

Seeing that his younger brother Yamasachihiko was blessed with good luck, his heart grew bitter and jealous, and finally Umisachihiko attacked him. So Yamasachihiko picked out the Shiomitsu Ball, and prayed for water and a great amount of water came and nearly caused his brother to drown.

Even when Umisachihiko ran up a high mountain, the water still reached there. He climbed a tall tree, but the water came up to its highest branches. He begged, "Please forgive me, I will be your servant from now on, please withdraw the water."

So Yamasachihiko prayed to the Shiohi Ball to remove the water, and the water withdrew.

Umisachihiko came to serve as his brother's vassal, knowing that he had excellent virtues. It was said the elder brother was the ancestor of the Hayato family. The Hayato clan have guarded the palace of the Emperor ever since.

During ceremonies, members of the Hayato clan paint red soil on their palms or face and make gestures with their bodies to symbolize turbulent water. They also make barking sounds like a dog.

日本語訳

海幸彦（うみさちひこ）と山幸彦（やまさちひこ）

むかし、はるかむかし、海には暖かい潮が流れ、たくさんの魚たちが泳いでいました。太陽は明るく輝き、山は深い緑におおわれ、鳥や動物たちがたくさんいました。

日本の南の地方、九州の今の宮崎県地方の物語です。

ここに、ふたりの青年がいました。ふたりとも高貴な神の御子（みこ）でした。兄は、魚釣り（さかなつ）にたくみで、釣りに行けば釣れない魚はなかったため、海幸彦と呼ばれていました。弟は、山や野原を駆けまわり、鳥や動物の狩りをしていたので、山幸彦と呼ばれていました。

ある日、山幸彦が言いました。

「毎日おなじことをしているのも、面白くない。私たちの道具をとりかえてみませんか」

兄はためらいましたが、弟が何度も熱心にくり返すので、その気になりました。

こうしてある日、山幸彦は兄の釣り針を借りうけて、海へ出かけることにしました。

弟は小舟を漕（こ）ぎだして、釣り糸を垂れてみたのですが、魚はまったく釣れませんでした。それまで、兄と同じくらいたくさんの魚が釣れて楽しめるとおもっていましたが、幸をもたらす釣り針は、持ち手がかわったとたんに、霊（れい）の力を失ってしまったのです。

しかも、釣っているうちに、大きな魚に釣り針を取られてしまま

いました。

山幸彦ががっかりして浜(はま)へもどると、兄も山からすでに帰ってきていて、おなじくがっくりしていました。弟の弓はやはり、持主の手を離(はな)れると役に立たなかったのでした。

弟はうなだれながら、釣り針を釣りでなくしてしまったことを告げました。兄は怒(おこ)りました。「あの釣り針は特別にたいせつにしていたものだ。すぐに捜し出して、返しなさい」

捜せといわれても、捜しようがありません。

弟は自分の剣(つるぎ)を潰(つぶ)して、たくさんの釣り針をつくりました。両の手のひらからこぼれるほどつくりました。

それを兄に差し出したのですが、「おまえに貸したあの釣り針がほしいのだ」と、兄は冷たくはねのけました。

弟は、途方(とほう)にくれて、渚(なぎさ)にたたずんでいました。思いあぐねて打ち沈(しず)んでいると、声をかける者がありました。

「どうして考えこんでおられるのです」

長い白いひげの老人が近寄ってきましたが、山幸彦は、この老人がどこから来たのか分かりませんでした。どうやって釣り針を捜したらよいのか途方に暮れていることを話すと、老人はにっこり笑ってうなずきました。この老人は、海の潮を支配するシオツチの翁(おきな)だったのです。

老人は、袋(ふくろ)のなかから黒い櫛(くし)を取り出し、それを大地に投げました。すると大地から、竹の子がはえ出て、みるみるうちに大きな竹となり、竹林になりました。老人はその竹を切って、目の詰(つ)まった竹(たけ)の籠(かご)の舟を編(あ)みあげました。

「これにお乗りなさい。よい海の潮が、あなたを海の神の宮殿へ導いてくれるでしょう。宮殿の門のそばには泉があって、大きな桂の木が茂っています。その木にのぼって待っていれば、ことはうまくいきます」

山幸彦は老人の言うとおりに、竹籠の舟に乗りました。舟はゆらりとひと揺れすると、見えない糸に引かれるかのように、沖へすべり出ていきました。

しばらくすると、舟のまわりには、いつか霧が立ちこめはじめて、それがしだいに深くなっていきましたが、はらりと消え失せて、美しい玉砂利を敷きつめた浜が見えました。

透き通った水に足を浸して、山幸彦はその浜へあがりました。やわらかい乳色の光に包まれた、不思議な世界でした。林を抜けると、美しい宮殿が現れました。門がある高い塀に囲まれた朱塗の高い楼閣がそびえていました。

門のかたわらに泉があり、泉のほとりには桂の木がありました。すべてシオツチの翁の言ったとおりです。山幸彦はためらわずに、その木によじのぼり、太い枝の一つにつかまりました。

どれほどの時が経ったのでしょう。門の中からお椀を持った侍女が出てきて、泉のそばへ近よりました。

水をくもうとして身をかがめた侍女は、水面に映る若い男の影を見て、びっくりして山幸彦を見上げました。

山幸彦は、ほほ笑みながら声をかけました。

「その清らかな水を一杯飲ましてください」

侍女が、言われるままに、水をくんで差し出すと、山幸彦は水を飲まず、首にかけていた勾玉を一つ取って口に含み、椀の中に吐き入れて返しました。

侍女は椀をすすぎながらとまどいました。山幸彦の吐き入れた勾玉が、椀の底にくっついてしまったからです。しかたなしに、そのまま泉の水を汲み入れて、椀を宮殿に持ち帰りました。

宮殿で、海の神の娘の豊玉姫は、侍女がささげたお椀の底に、光り輝く勾玉がくっついているを見て、気になりました。

「門の外にどなたかいらっしゃるのですか」と聞き、「麗しい、若い男の方がいらっしゃいました」と侍女は答えました。

豊玉姫が門のかげからそっとうかがうと、侍女の言葉どおり、麗しい若者が桂の枝に腰かけていました。

姫の知らせを聞いた海の神である父親のワダツミの神は、

「その方は、高貴な神の御子に違いない。丁寧にご案内しなさい」と言って、山幸彦を恭しく迎え入れました。

やがて若いふたりは、恋に落ちて、結婚しました。

毎日がめずらしく楽しく、山幸彦はその宮殿で３年の年月を過ごしました。

しかし、ある日、山幸彦は自分がここに来ることになった、ことの起こりを思い出しました。兄の釣り針は、まだ手に入っていません。それを思うと、深い溜息がもれました。もの思いに沈む夫のようすは豊玉姫の心を痛めました。

「３年の間、楽しくお暮らしになっていたのに、今日は深い溜息をおつきになった。父に相談しなければならない」と考えました。「何かあったのですか」とワダツミが尋ねてみると、山幸彦は、「失った兄の釣り針を捜しています」と答えました。

そこでワダツミがすぐに、ありとあらゆる魚たちを集めて釣り針のことを聞きましたが、誰もそのような針は知りませんでした。そのうち、ある魚が思い出して言いました。

「そういえば、鯛が近ごろ喉を痛めて、物を食べられないと嘆いていると言っている者がいました」。そこでワダツミは、鯛を呼び出してその喉を探ると、はたして山幸彦の失った釣り針が出てきました。

ワダツミは釣り針を洗いきよめて、山幸彦に捧げました。求めていた釣り針が手に入ると、山幸彦の心を引きとめるすべがないことを知って、姫は悲しみました。

ワダツミは別れにあたって、山幸彦にこまごまと注意をあたえました。

「この釣り針をお兄さんに返すときは、うしろ向きになって、『くるしみ針、いらいら針、貧乏針、おろか針』と唱えながら、投げ返しなさい。そうすれば、針は霊の力を失ってしまうでしょう。

それから、お兄さんが高いところに田をつくったら、あなたは低いところにつくり、お兄さんが低いところにつくったら、あなたは高いところにつくりなさい。私は水を司る者だから、あなたの田にだけ水が行くようにできます。

お兄さんが舟に乗って釣りに出かけたら、あなたは岸辺に立って、口をすぼめて海のほうへ息を吹きなさい。すぐに私が大風を起こして、お兄さんの舟を覆します。

そのようにしていると、３年のうちに、お兄さんはすっかり貧しくなってしまわれるでしょう。そして、あなたを恨んで攻めかかってこられるかもしれません。

そのときは、この塩満の玉と塩干の玉とをお使いなさい。塩満

の玉を持って、あなたが『水よ起これ』と心に念じれば、大水が来ます。塩干の玉は、『水よ退け』と念じれば、たちまち水を引き退けます」

そう言って、２つの玉を山幸彦に授けました。

さてワダツミは、鮫たちを呼び集めて、

「神の御子が陸の国へお帰りになる。汝ら、何日でお送りできるか」と聞きました。鮫たちは、自分のからだの大きさや鰭の強さを考えながら、日数を見積もって返答しましたが、一尋鮫は、「私なら即座に国へお送りして、その日のうちにご報告いたします」と答えた。海の神は、「それでは、汝を遣わそう。海を渡るときは、恐ろしい思いをさせることを禁じる」と言って、一尋鮫に、山幸彦を送り届ける役目を許可しました。

一尋鮫は、すばやく山幸彦を陸に送り届けました。

弟は兄に会って、釣り針を返しました。海の神に言われたとおりにしたことは、言うまでもありません。

霊能を失った釣り針を受け取った兄は、それ以来、釣りをしても、魚がいっこうに釣れず、おまけに大風が吹いて舟が転覆してしまいました。

高いところに田をつくれば、日照りが続いて水に困り、低いところに田をつくれば、雨が降り続いて、水浸しになります。３年も経ったら貧しくなってしまいました。

ワダツミの言ったとおりです。

そして弟が、幸運に恵まれるのを見て、恨んで妬み心を起こし、とうとう弟に襲いかかりました。

そこで弟は、塩満の玉を取り出して、水よ起これと念じると、大水が起こって、兄をおぼれかけさせました。海幸彦が高い山に駆(か)け上がっても、水はそこにまで達しました。高い木に登りましたが、その木の高い枝にまで水は押し寄せてきました。

兄は、「許してくれ、私はこれからおまえのしもべになって、仕えよう。どうか水を退(しりぞ)けてくれ」と許しを請(こ)いました。そこで山幸彦が、潮干の玉に、水よ退けと念じると、水が引きました。

海幸彦は、弟が優れた徳を備えていることを知って、家臣として仕えるようになりました。この兄は、隼人族(はやとぞく)の祖先にあたるとされています。

隼人族は、以来、天皇の宮殿をお守りしてきました。

儀式のときには、隼人族は、赤土を手のひらや顔に塗って、荒(あ)れ狂(くる)う水のようなしぐさを見せています。また、彼らは犬のように、吠(ほ)える声を発したりもします。

Track
#03

Gyoran Kannon

魚籃観音

ぎょらんかんのん

Statue of Buddha with the spiritual power to allow people of faith to get a rich harvest of fish.

Miyazaki City is the capital of Miyazaki Prefecture in Japan.

Awakigahara Town is located in Miyazaki City. There is a beach around the town. Native people call the beach Hitotsubahama (Hitotsuba Beach) where the mouth of Oyodo River made an inlet. We can see white sand and green pines alongside the long beach. It's a very beautiful place. The main inlet connects to many smaller inlets and we can also see lines of pine trees further in the distance. Here myths and legends remain. This part is sacred land and called Tachibana no Odo no Aokigahara, where Izanagi no Mikoto (God of Izanagi) performed purity rituals.

A long time ago, a young fisherman was casting a net to catch fish into the inlet of Hitotsubahama every morning. On one hot early morning he habitually cast his net, but he didn't catch any fish until sunset. Giving up on the fishing, he decided to go home, when a young lady who was dressed as a fisherperson appeared from the wood of pine trees. She was walking toward the young man along the shore. When they crossed each other, he looked at her bamboo basket on her shoulders and was surprised to see a lot of seabasses which dazzled with silver color.

On the next day he continued to cast his net into the water, but again could catch nothing. He was preparing to come home, when again the fisherwoman he met yesterday passed by him. He couldn't help but look into her basket. Many big seabasses were springing out of it. His lips moved subconsciously, "Where did you get those fish?" She replied, "Sir, learn by heart completely the Sutra of Kannon (Buddhist scriptures), then throw your net into the sea while chanting the sutra", then she walked away hastily.

As soon as the fisherman returned home, he read the sutra, and read, read, and reread without sleeping the whole night.

The next morning he cast the net into Hitotsubahama while chanting the sutra to himself. After a while when he was pulling the net in, he felt a heavy weight in his hands. He saw a statue of Kannon glittering like gold in the bottom of the net. He picked it up and gazed at it. It was a holy statue carved from a camphor tree and was about 45.5 cm

high, holding a basket for fish in its hands. Because he felt it was holy and wondrous, he thought he should dedicate this Kannon to Shokou Buddhist temple in the Ukinojou Area in Aoki Village.

Soon he passed through the gate of the temple, where a lady who really resembled that fisherwoman was standing glancing at him. She stepped up to him.

"You are Mr. Yosoemon, aren't you? I just came here from Kunisaki Peninsula in Bungo State (now Oita Prefecture, which is adjacent to the northern border of Miyazaki Prefecture) this morning.

According to the calling of Kannon my future husband is Mr. Yosoemon who lives in Naka Village in Hyuga State (now Sumiyoshi Town in Miyazaki City), so I came here all the way from Kunisaki Peninsula," she said to him.

When she caught sight of the man who was going up the hill holding a Kannon flashing like gold in his hands, she realized that he could be Yosoemon. The fisherman agreed to marry her.

After this event the rich harvest of fish continued and as soon as the fisherman's wife went to sell them in town, she sold out in no time.

In fact, the man's name was Shimizu Yosoemon who later

became the richest man around Naka Village.

The statue was called Gyoran Kannon (Kannon holding a bamboo basket for carrying fish) or Amikake Kannon (throwing net Kannon), and was stored in Houjuzan Shoukou Temple and till this day the statue is worshipped by many people.

The reason that the temple was named Shoukou Temple (shou and kou mean ‘true’ and ‘light’ respectively in Japanese) was that the Kannon was shining at the bottom of the sea. There are some legends about the building of Shoukou Temple. The temple was built by Kagekiyo who was a samurai belonging to the Heike Family (a warrior family about eight hundred years ago in Japan.).

日本語訳

魚籃観音

正直な人々に豊かな魚の収穫をもたらす
不思議な力を持った仏像。

宮崎市は、日本の宮崎県の県都です。

宮崎市には阿波岐原町があります。町のそばには、浜辺があります。この地方の人々は、この浜辺を一ツ葉浜と呼んでおり、ここに大淀川の河口が入江をつくっています。白砂青松の長い渚が続いていて、非常に美しいところです。入江には、さらに細長い入江がいくつも入り込んでいて、その奥にまた松林があります。この辺りは神話と伝説が残されていて、神聖な地と伝えられており、橘の小戸の檍原と呼ばれ、伊弉諾尊が禊祓いをした場所です。

むかしのことです。若い漁師がこの一ツ葉の入江で、毎朝、網を投げ入れていました。

ある暑い朝のこと、漁師はいつものように朝早くから網を投げ入れていましたが、日が西に傾きかける頃になっても魚は一匹も取れませんでした。漁をあきらめて引き揚げようとすると、松林の中から漁師姿の若い娘が現れて、浜辺づたいにこちらにやって来ました。すれちがいざまに娘の肩の魚籠をのぞくと、銀色に光る鱸がいっぱいに入っていたので、驚いてしまいました。

次の日も、漁師は水に網を投げ入れ続けていましたが、やはり雑魚一匹かかりませんでした。帰り支度をしていると、また昨日の女の漁師が通りかかりました。彼は彼女の籠を見ずにはおれませんでした。その中で、たくさんのみごとな鱸が飛びはねていました。漁師が思わず、「どこでその魚を捕ったのか」と声をかけた。その娘は、「観音経をそらんじなされ。観音経を唱えながら、海に網を入れてみなされ」と答え、足早に立ち去っていきました。

家に帰るや否や、漁師は夜どおし経文をそらんじて、翌朝、それを唱えながら一ツ葉浜に網を投げ入れました。しばらくして網を引き揚げながら、彼は両手にずっしりと重みを感じました。

すると網の底には、黄金色に輝く観音像があるではありませんか。網から取り出してながめてみると、それは楠を刻んだ45.5㎝ほどの御像で、魚籃（びく）を手にしていました。あまりに尊く、見事だったので、漁師はこの観音像を檍村の浮之城にある正光寺に奉納しなければならないと思いました。すぐに寺の山門をくぐりかけると、例の娘によく似た女の漁師がたたずんでいて、彼を見るなり近寄ってきました。

「あなたは四十右衛門さんでしょう。私は豊後（現在の宮崎県の北側に隣接する大分県）の国東半島から今朝、ここに着いたばかりです。

観音様のお告げで自分の夫になるのは日向の国の那珂村（現在の宮崎市住吉町）に住む四十右衛門だと知らされ、国東半島からはるばる訪ねてまいりました」と娘は言いました。

彼女は黄金のように輝く観音様を抱えて丘を登ってくる男を見たとたん、娘はこの男性が四十右衛門に違いないと思いました。漁師は女を妻に迎え入れました。それからは驚くほど豊漁が続

き、捕れた魚は、妻が町に売りに行けばまたたく間に売れました。この男性の名前こそ、のちに那珂村あたりで一番の分限者（金持ち）となった清水四十右衛門です。

この仏像は、魚籃観音（魚籠を抱えた観音）、またの名を網掛観音（網を投げ入れる観音）と呼ばれて、宝寿山正光寺に安置され、いまなお多くの人から信仰を集めています。寺の名を正光寺というのは、観音像が海中から光を発していたからです（「正」および「光」は、日本語でそれぞれ真実、光を意味します）。この正光寺の建立については、伝説があり、平家（日本における約800年前の武士団）の武将、景清によって建てられたものであるといわれています。

Track #04

Okuragahama Story

お倉ヶ浜物語

Once upon a time there was a girl in the Hiraiwa District (Present-day Hiraiwa of Hyuga City in Miyazaki Prefecture in Japan) who was named Okane.

One day at the end of summer she said, "It's fine today and the tide is good. So I'm going to dig clams at the shore." So in the early morning hours she went to the shore. She didn't see any people there, and white waves were quietly coming up and down in turns.

Okane at once walked into the water up to her ankles, and she began digging clams. Clams here were fine and big. Some of them were ten centimeters wide. They received the waves and danced this way and that on the sand.

"Wow! I found a good one here by my left toes!" she exclaimed, "and another one, this is huge!"

She was gathering them not noticing anything around her for a long time. She dug up the clams and put them into her bamboo basket again and again.

A Buddhist priest was watching Okane working for some

time before he walked down to her via a path leading to the beach. He wore a black coat and a straw (sedge) hat. His hands were covered with white patches. He looked like a pilgrim on the way to his training tour. The priest approached her, and peering at her basket, exclaimed, "Oh! Magnificent clams! I have never seen such clams!" Then he said to her, "In fact lady, I could be donated a couple of those." Okane's happy expression suddenly changed, and she put the basket behind her back. "These are not clams, all of them are stones," she said calmly. The priest cocked his head a little to one side, and mumbled, "Is it true, surely they aren't all stones, are they? They don't look like stones to me," and he walked away along the beach.

At the next beach another girl, Okura, was also digging clams. The priest spoke to her too. "These are good clams, aren't they? I would like a couple of clams too." "Yes Priest, if you want these sorts of clams, you can take them as you wish," said Okura. She willingly gave him the clams. The priest politely bowed to her and said, "These are much appreciated gifts. If I eat them, I will be energized. You are a very compassionate person. As Buddha will certainly get to know your kind mind, this beach will permanently yield clams in the future." The priest said with a smile. Okura blushed

slightly and nodded her head. Then the priest walked away, his figure gradually fading on the shore's horizon.

After the priest's prayer, Okura's beach suddenly began to produce many clams and still does to this day. But mysteriously, in spite of sharing the same shore of Hiraiwa, Okane's beach wouldn't yield any clams at all. Since then, the people of the Hiraiwa District have called the beaches Okuragahama and Okanegahama (Beach of Okura and Beach of Okane).

To this day the area has crafted white *goishi.* A set of white *goishi* and black *goishi* are used when you play *igo*, a Japanese board game (including *shogi*) similar to the western game of chess.

The black *goishi* is crafted from stone from other places around Japan. The white *goishi* is a two centimeter diameter circle cut from the center of a clam shell.

White *goishi* made in Okuragahama Hyuga City has now been declared the best in all of Japan.

日本語訳

お倉ヶ浜物語

むかしむかし、平岩地区（現在の日本の宮崎県日向市平岩）にお金、という名前の娘がいました。

ある夏の終わりの日に娘は言いました。

「今日は晴れていい日だな、潮の流れもよい。よし、浜辺へはまぐりを取りに行こう」

朝早く、娘は海辺に行きました。そこには誰もいませんでした。そして白い波が静かに寄せては離れていました。

お金は、すぐくるぶしが浸かるぐらい水の中に入り、砂を掘ってはまぐりを採りはじめました。この辺りのはまぐりは、大きくて立派でした。中には10cmもあるものさえありました。それらのはまぐりが波を受けながら、砂の上をころころ転がっていました。

「わあー、左足の指のそばにいいはまぐりがある」と叫びました。「あそこには、大きいのがある」

彼女は、夢中になって長い間、はまぐりを採っていました。何度も何度も砂を掘っては、はまぐりを採り竹かごに入れました。

あるお坊さんが、しばらくの間、お金がはまぐりを採っているのをじっと見ていました。そして浜辺へ続く小道を通り、彼女の方へ歩いていきました。お坊さんは黒い衣に編笠をかぶっていました。彼の手には白い布あてが付けられていました。彼は諸国を行脚している修行僧のようでした。そのお坊さんは、お金に近づき、彼女の竹かごの中を見て、驚いて叫び声をあげました。

「見事なはまぐりじゃのう。こんなはまぐりは見たことがない」

それからお坊さんは、続けて言いました。

「ところで娘さん、そのはまぐりを2、3個、私にめぐんではくださらんか」。お金は、突然顔色を変えました。そして竹かごを背中の方へ隠しました。

「これらは、はまぐりじゃない。みんな石じゃ」と彼女はとぼけて言いました。それを聞いたお坊さんは、頭を少しかしげてつぶやきながら言いました。

「それは本当かね。みんな石ではないのではないかな。私には石には見えないがね」

そうしてお坊さんは、その浜辺から立ち去りました。

次の浜辺では、別な娘、お倉がはまぐりを採っていました。お坊さんは、また彼女に声をかけました。

「見事なはまぐりじゃのう。2、3個そのはまぐりを、私にもくださらんか」

「ああ、お坊さん、こんなはまぐりでよかったら、いくらでも持って行ってください」とお倉は答えました。

彼女は喜んではまぐりを、お坊さんにさしあげました。お坊さんは丁寧に頭を下げて彼女に言いました。

「これらはありがたい贈りもんじゃ。私はこれを食べたら、また元気が出るじゃろう。あなたは本当に優しい心を持った人だ。仏様は、必ずあなたの優しい気持ちを知るじゃろうから、今後ずーっとこの浜辺では、はまぐりが採れるじゃろう」とお坊さんはほほえんで言いました。

お倉はほほを少し赤くして、お坊さんに頭を下げました。それ

からお坊さんは歩いて遠ざかり、その姿は少しずつ浜辺の地平線から見えなくなりました。

このお坊さんのお恵(めぐ)みの後、お倉がいた浜辺では、突然(とつぜん)、たくさんのはまぐりが、採れるようになり、それが今日(こんにち)まで続いています。しかしながら、同じ平岩の海岸の浜辺であるにもかかわらず、お金がいた浜辺では、不思議にも全くはまぐりが採れなくなりました。平岩地区の人々が、これらの浜辺をそれぞれ、「お倉ヶ浜」「お金ヶ浜」と呼ぶようになったのは、この頃(ころ)からでした。

今日(こんにち)までこの地方では、白の碁石(ごいし)がつくられてきました。

白の碁石と黒の碁石は囲碁(いご)をするときに使われ、このゲームは（将棋とともに）西洋のチェスと似ています。黒の碁石は、日本のほかの地域でつくられます。白の碁石は、はまぐりをくりぬいて直径２cmの丸い形につくられています。

今日、日向市のお倉ヶ浜でつくられる白碁石は、日本で最高の品質だといわれています。

Track #05

Kagekiyo and His Daughter Hitomaru

景清とその娘人丸

Around 800 years ago the Genji, an ancient samurai family, and the Heike, the opposition samurai family, had repeated fierce battles. But finally the Heike were defeated in Dannoura (which is now located in Shimonoseki City in Yamaguchi Prefecture in Japan).

At this time, the Heike's samurai, Aku Shichibei Kagekiyo, secretly escaped by swimming out to sea.

Aku Shichibei is a nickname, which means brave man. His family name is Fujiwara and given name is Kagekiyo. He is always called by his nickname.

(In this story names are written in the order family name first, then given name, as is the custom in Japanese culture.)

He planned to attack the chief commander of Genji, Yoritomo, as revenge for the Heike attack, if the chance arose in the future.

One May, Minamoto (family name) Yoritomo (given name), decided to visit Todai Temple to pray in Nara (present-day Nara City of Nara Prefecture).

When Kagekiyo heard this news, he put on clothes dyed black and a deep hood on his head and disguised himself as a soldier monk. He went out to Todai Temple, hiding a short sword in his light green knitted waist band.

However, Kagekiyo's plan was completely foiled. Bccausc he was a giant over 180 centimeters in height, he was immediately noticed and caught by a Genji samurai who questioned him.

Kagekiyo was pulled out in front of Yoritomo by the Genji's commander Hatakeyama Shigetada. Yoritomo understood the pure loyalty of Kagekiyo to his lord in carrying out his will. He was moved by it so much that he spared the life of Kagekiyo and decided to exile him to Hyuga of Kyushu in Japan (present-day Miyazaki Prefecture on Kyushu island).

Kagekiyo often thought that he would kill himself, but he could not go through with it, and instead he became a priest and settled in the Shimokitakata District of Hyuga country (now Shimokitakata Town of Miyazaki City). He built a small grass hut on the hill of Shimokitakata, and made a living, while chanting Namuamidabutsu and trying to seek the way of truth in Buddhism.

On a sunny autumn day, Kagekiyo was gazing at the flow of Oyodo River from the top of a hill. In wide fields, golden ears of ripe rice were waving below him. It was a mild harvest day.

Although he had become a priest, Kagekiyo had not yet understood his enlightenment. He was irritated and felt uneasy.

"It is a world for the Genji to thrive, but the Heike will never see the sunlight again, and even if I can see it, I am worried I will not enter the way of Buddha forever. In the end I have to throw away my good eyes so as not to see Genji's prosperity."

Kagekiyo murmured as if he had gone mad, and stabbed his fingers into his eyes. Then he grabbed both eyes and threw them away as far as he could into the sky. The place where Kagekiyo's eyes landed, was called Ikime (which means 'the living eyes' in Japanese, and is the current Ikime District in Miyazaki City). There Ikime Shrine has since been enshrined as the place of the god of healthy eyes.

Kagekiyo who threw away both his eyes and went blind, became more involved in the way of Buddha, and became a 'biwa' player (biwa is an ancient Japanese stringed instrument), traveling around the villages for religious mendicancy.

Kagekiyo had a daughter whose name was Hitomaru.

From a young age she was left in a wealthy person's care in Kamakura which was once the Japanese capital, now known as Kamakura City in Kanagawa Prefecture. But Hitomaru happened to hear that her father was exiled far away to Hyuga country.

"Is my father living well? I wish to see him," she thought. Hitomaru was concerned about her father.

"I would like to meet my father ...so I will go to visit him," Hitomaru decided.

Even though she was a frail woman, Hitomaru set off on the long journey from Kamakura in the company of only one follower.

She walked from Kamakura to Kyoto and then continued further west. It was hard work for the person who traced the road toward Chikushi. Chikushi is now known as present-day Fukuoka Prefecture in Japan, and is the entrance to Kyushu Island.

While having an image in mind of her precious father, Hitomaru eventually reached Hyuga.

Hitomaru went up the hill of Shimokitakata. She heard that her father Kagekiyo lived here. She thought she had at last reached the land where her father lived, and her tired legs suddenly started getting stronger.

Hitomaru went past the houses of poor farmers scattered over the hill and stopped to look into a small thatched hut.

Someone was living in the hut. "Shall I ask here?" Hitomaru approached the front of the hut with her follower.

A shadow of a figure moved inside.

"Excuse me, I wonder if there is an exile of the Heike around here."

As if the person was surprised at the voice of Hitomaru, the answer returned quickly. "Exile of what? Heike? What is their name?"

"Their name is Aku Shichibei Kagekiyo," Hitomaru replied.

"Yes, but I don't know them. Kagekiyo?! ... no, who is it? Anyway, I'm blind, please ask somewhere else."

The voice that sounded from inside the hut was trembling. It was strange, Hitomaru thought. However, night was already approaching, and the face of the person in the hut was hard to see.

Hitomaru gave up and walked away from the hut.

However, the sole resident in the hut was none other than her dearest father Kagekiyo, who Hitomaru had been asking

for.

Kagekiyo recognized Hitomaru's voice, and he wanted badly to run out and hold her hand.

However, he did not want to disgrace himself in her presence. So he deliberately told the lie, and avoided Hitomaru.

Kagekiyo's heart was wrung in pain, hearing the footsteps that faded away in the distance. It was pitiful. It was painful. Kagekiyo, crouched in his dimly lit hut, was holding back the tears.

Hitomaru visited a farmer's house a little way away from Kagekiyo's hut when the farmer said something surprising. "The blind person who lives in the grass hut that you passed is Kagekiyo."

Hitomaru was struck in the heart with shock. Tears welled up in her eyes. She wondered if her father didn't understand her to be his daughter.

But then her follower asked the farmer, "Excuse me, but would you please call Kagekiyo? It seems that Kagekiyo did not give his name because he was ashamed of himself from the circumstance of exile."

The farmer nodded and took Hitomaru to Kagekiyo's hut immediately. "Is Kagekiyo here? Aku Shichibei Kagekiyo!"

"Who are you? Why do you call my name?" from inside the hut the low voice of Kagekiyo returned.

The farmer was nodding to himself and gestured toward Hitomaru. Without a doubt, the inhabitant of the hut was Kagekiyo.

Hitomaru entered the hut to endure her sorrow and sidled in front of her father. "Dearest Father! I came here from Kamakura. I'm Hitomaru!"

"What, Hitomaru? I don't know a Hitomaru. Who is Hitomaru?"

"Why are you saying this? Father, I remember your face even though we were separated since I was very young." Hitomaru's voice was trembling.

She had a desperate desire to hear him say the word 'daughter'.

Soon a deep sigh passed from Kagekiyo's lips. He gave up pretending and murmured softly, "Hitomaru, I understand. It is amazing that a woman like you came here from far away. But this Kagekiyo is a recluse, and there is no place for you. However, even if a person abandons the world, the ties of the parent and child can't be cut."

Hitomaru involuntarily grasped the trembling hands of Kagekiyo. Kagekiyo also held Hitomaru's shoulder and tears welled in his invisible eyes.

From that day forth, Hitomaru lived in the grounds of Shimokitakata and, she served her blind father every day, and took care of his surroundings. The father and daughter lived quietly joining their hands in prayer every morning and evening, and chanting the sutra.

The villagers were kind to Kagekiyo and Hitomaru, especially to the young Hitomaru who came from a place far away from the capital. When they saw her taking care of her father kindly, they praised her in chorus, "She is a dutiful daughter."

Sadly, Hitomaru passed away suddenly at the young age of 24 years old due to illness. The people in the village mourned her death, and they built her grave in the ground of Shimokitakata, and called it 'the dutiful daughter Hitomaru's grave'.

After losing Hitomaru, Kagekiyo traveled around villages for religious mendicancy, while playing the biwa.

He fell ill on the way back from Kirishima Shrine, and he died at some place. His corpse was carried to the hill in Shimokitakata, and his grave was built there alongside Hitomaru's. The fragrant smoke of incense sticks always lingers around their graves even today. (In Japan when a human died, their family and other persons concerned mourn the death of the human. At that moment of prayer, they lower their heads and burn incense in front of the dead or grave. This custom originates in Buddhist ritual.)

日本語訳

景清とその娘人丸

およそ800年のむかしのことです。

源氏と平氏は、はげしい戦いをくりかえしていましたが、とうとう壇ノ浦（日本の現在の山口県下関市にあります）で、平氏が負けてしまいました。

このとき、悪七兵衛景清という平家の侍は、こっそり海を泳いで逃げ延びました。悪七兵衛は通称で、勇敢な男という意味です。本当の姓は藤原、名は景清と言いますが、彼は通称でとおっていました。

彼は、いつかすきを見て源氏の総大将、頼朝の命をねらい、平家のあだを討とうと思っていました。

ある年の５月の頃、源頼朝は、奈良の東大寺にお参りすることにしました。

景清はこの話を聞くと、さっそく墨染めの衣に、すっぽりと頭巾をかぶって、僧兵に化けました。そして、もえぎ色の腹巻に短刀をしのばせて、東大寺に出かけて行きました。

ところが景清のたくらみは、まんまと見破られてしまいました。景清は、180cmを超える大男だったので、それを素早く見とがめたある源氏の侍に、つかまってしまったのです。

景清は、源氏の大将畠山重忠によって、頼朝の前に引き出されました。

頼朝は景清が主君のあだ討ちをしようとする志を知った。心を打たれた頼朝は、景清の命をたすけて、日本の九州、日向に流すことにしました。

景清は、何回か死のうと思いましたが、それを果たせず、出家して、日向の国の下北方地区（今の宮崎市下北方町）へたどり着きました。景清は、下北方の丘の上に、小さな草ぶきの小屋を建てて、念仏を唱えながら、仏の道を求めて、暮らすようになりました。

ある晴れた秋の日に、景清は丘の上から、じっと大淀川の流れを見つめていました。眼下の広い田んぼには、黄金の稲穂が波打っていました。のどかな取り入れの日でした。

出家はしたものの、景清は、まだ悟りをひらいていませんでした。なんとなく心がいら立って、落ち着きませんでした。

「源氏の世はさかえ、平家は再び日の目を見ることはあるまい。それが見えるばかりに、拙者は、いつまでも仏の道に入れないで悩んでいる。そうだ、このけん眼（健康な目）をすてて、源氏の繁栄に目をつぶらねばならない」

景清はそうつぶやくと、狂ったように、自分の２つの目に指を突き立てました。そうして両眼をえぐり取るなり、空のかなたに力いっぱい投げ捨てました。景清が投げた両眼が落ちたところは、生目（今の宮崎市生目）と呼ばれました。生目には、目の神様として生目神社がまつられています。

両眼をすてて盲目となった景清は、ますます仏の道にはげんで、琵琶法師となり、托鉢のために村々をまわっていました。

景清には、人丸という一人の娘がいました。

人丸は、幼い頃から、鎌倉のある長者の家に預けられていました。鎌倉はかつて日本の主府となり、現在は神奈川県の鎌倉市となっています。風の便りに、父景清が日向の国に流されていることを聞きました。

「父上は、達者でおられるのだろうか。父上に会いたい」と思い、人丸は、父のことが気がかりでした。

「父上に会いたい……。父のもとを訪ねよう」

人丸は決心しました。

人丸はか弱い女の身でありながら、一人の供を連れただけで、鎌倉から遠くへ旅立ちました。

鎌倉から京都へ、京都から西へ西へと歩き続けて、筑紫路(ちくしじ)をたどる人丸の苦労は、並大抵ではありませんでした。筑紫は日本の現在の福岡県(ふくおかけん)にあたり、九州の入り口です。

人丸は恋しい父の面影(おもかげ)を胸にいだいて、やがて日向までたどり着きました。

人丸は、下北方の丘の道を登っていきました。この地に父景清が住んでいると聞いたのです。とうとう父の住む土地にたどり着いたと思うと、人丸の疲(つか)れた足も急に軽くなりました。

人丸は、丘の上に散らばっている貧しいお百姓(ひゃくしょう)の家を通り過ぎて、小さな草ぶきの小屋に目を留め、立ち止まりました。

小屋には誰か住んでいました。

「あの小屋で尋ねてみましょうか」

人丸は供人(ともびと)とともに、小屋の前に近づきました。小屋の中で人影(ひとかげ)が動きました。

「もし、この辺りに平家の流人はいませんでしょうか」

人丸の声に驚いたように、返事がすぐ返ってきました。

「なに、平家の流人。その名は誰か」

「はい、その名は悪七兵衛景清ともうしますが」と人丸は答えました。

「景清……。いや、それは存ぜぬぞ。だれかな。なにぶん拙者はめしいの身、どうかよそでお尋ねください」

小屋の中から響(ひび)いてくる声は震(ふる)えていました。人丸は不思議に思いました。しかし、もう夕やみがせまっていて、小屋の中の人の顔はよく見えませんでした。人丸はあきらめて、小屋から立ち去りました。

ところが、小屋の住人こそ、人丸が訪ねていたなつかしい父、ほかならない景清だったのです。

景清には、人丸の声におぼえがありました。ほんとうなら、すぐにでも小屋を出て、人丸の手を握(にぎ)りたかったのです。

しかし景清は、おちぶれた哀(あわ)れな姿を、娘の前にさらしたくありませんでした。そこで、わざと偽(いつわ)りを言って、人丸を避(さ)けたのです。

景清は遠のいていく人丸の足音を聞きながら、胸をかきむしられるようにつらい思いをしました。

あわれなことじゃ。せつないことじゃ。

景清は薄暗(うすぐら)い小屋の中にうずくまって、じっと涙(なみだ)をこらえていました。

人丸は、景清の小屋から少し離れたお百姓の家を訪ねると、そのお百姓さんはけげんそうに言いました。

「おまえさまが、いま通り過ぎてきなさった草ぶきの小屋に住んでおられるめしいの方が、景清さまじゃ」

人丸は、はっと胸をつかれました。まぶたに涙が込み上げてきました。父は娘の私が分からなかったのでしょうか。

しかしその時、供人がそのお百姓さんに声をかけました。

「すみませんが、あなたが景清さまを呼んでくださいませんでしょうか。景清さまは、流人の身をはじて、なのりなさらなかったことと思われます」

お百姓さんはうなずくと、さっそく人丸を景清の小屋に連れていきました。

「景清さまはいなさるか。悪七兵衛景清さま」

「誰じゃ。拙者の名を呼ぶものは」

小屋の中から、景清の低い声が返ってきました。

お百姓さんはこっくりとして、人丸にうなずいて見せました。まちがいなく、小屋の住人は景清でした。人丸は、悲しみをこらえて小屋に入り、父の前ににじり寄りました。

「父上、鎌倉から父上を訪ねてまいりました、人丸でございます」

「何、人丸じゃと。人丸などという者は、拙者はしらぬぞ。人丸とは誰かな」

「父上、何をおっしゃいます。幼い頃に別れたきりとはいえ、私は父上のお顔をよおくおぼえております」

人丸の声は震えていました。父に一言、娘と呼んでもらいたいという、必死の思いが込められていました。やがて景清の口から、深いため息がもれました。景清は、わが身を偽ることをあきらめて、小さな声でそっとつぶやきました。

「人丸、わかったぞ。女の身でよくここまで訪ねて来てくれたものじゃ。この景清は世捨て人で、お前に合わす顔はない。だが、いくら世を捨てても、親子の縁(えん)は切れないものじゃ」

人丸は思わず、震える景清の手を握りしめました。景清も人丸の肩を抱いて、見えない目に涙をうかべました。

この日から人丸は、この下北方の地に住むことになりました。そして毎日、めしいの父に仕えて、身まわりの世話をしました。

父と娘は朝夕、仏様に手を合わせて、念仏をとなえながら、静かな暮らしを続けました。

村人たちは、景清にも人丸にも、とくに都から遠く離れた地に来た若い人丸に親切でした。人丸がやさしく父景清をいたわっているすがたを見ると、

「感心で、孝行な娘さんじゃわい」

と、口をそろえてほめていました。

ところが、人丸はふとした病気がもとで、24歳(さい)の若さで、ぽっくりと亡くなってしまったのです。

村の人々は、人丸の死を悲しんで、下北方の地に墓を建て、孝女人丸の墓と呼びました。

人丸を亡くした景清は、その後も琵琶をひきながら、村々の托鉢に回りました。が、霧島神宮の参拝の帰り道に、病に倒れて、あるところで亡くなりました。

景清の亡骸(なきがら)は、下北方の丘に運ばれて、人丸と並んで墓が建てられました。ふたりの墓には、いまでも、線香(せんこう)の煙(けむり)が絶えません。

(日本では、人が死んだ時、その家族や関係者は人の死を悼みます。その際、死者や墓の前で頭を下げ、線香を焚(た)きます。この習慣は仏教が由来です。)

Track #06

The Chapped Boy

あかぎれ少年

Mt. Sobo is a famous 1,760 -meter high mountain on the borders of the Hyuga State (now Miyazaki Prefecture in Japan), Bungo State (Oita Prefecture), and Higo State (Kumamoto Prefecture).

A long time ago there lived a rich tycoon called Shioda no Taifu. He had a daughter who was like a beautiful flower. Her name was Hana no Mimoto, which means 'a genuine flower'.

As she grew up to become a lady of marriageable age, there were many proposals from far and wide. But her father couldn't give her to any young person, because he loved Mimoto the most. He built a cottage near the main house in his estate and made her live alone, treating her with great care.

Whenever the bright moon came out at night, the melody of a distant Japanese flute was always heard in Shioda Village.

"Who is the person that can create this most beautiful melody of the flute?" puzzled villagers would think to themselves as they came out onto the tiny road.

Under the bright moonlight they would see an elegant

young man who wore a hunting uniform (a type of formal dress in old Japanese times), and a long vertical hat (called 'eboshi' in Japanese, similar to a derby or bowler hat) quietly walking the streets.

"Hmmm. We have never seen that nice young man in our village. What's happening? Where is he from and where does he go to?" They would think and discuss amongst themselves. But no one knew anything at all about him.

The young man would walk through the pass playing the flute, and soon he would go through the gates to the tycoon's house, without being seen by anyone. Like the wind he would silently sneak into the yard, he never failed to visit Mimoto's room. He would tell her many interesting stories. Then, as the eastern sky was beginning to brighten, he would return from where he came.

Mimoto couldn't understand where this charming young man came from, nor did she know who he was.

Soon her parents noticed that the young man would visit Mimoto's room to talk and enjoy himself on moonlit nights. Mimoto's mother instructed her, "You have to find out exactly where he is from and and who he is. You mustn't entertain or talk with him unless that is clear."

Mimoto replied, "But mother, whenever I ask him who he

is, he says nothing."

"In that case I have a good idea," said her mother. "I will give you a needle and a spool with thread. Next time he comes, you should stick the needle into the collar of his clothes. He will return to his home with the threaded needle on his clothes, so you will only have to follow the thread to learn where he returns to. Don't forget!"

On the night of a full moon the young man visited Mimoto's room, sounding the beautiful music of his flute as usual. While Mimoto was talking and entertaining him, obeying her mother's orders she stuck the needle into the collar of his clothes without him realizing. At dawn, as usual, the young man returned to where he came none-the-wiser.

Shioda no Taifu and Mimoto searched for the young man by following the trail of thread with their loyal servants. The thread trailed on and on. They walked a long distance climbing hills, crossing rivers, and passing through woods. The thread led them alongside Mt. Sobo. At last, they reached the foothills of Mt. Sobo, and they climbed its slopes following the thread.

Finally, the line disappeared into a cave halfway up the mountain.

"Woooh, Wooooh." They heard terrible moans from inside

the cave. “How strange...” they wondered, as they stood in front of the cave.

Something was groaning and the voice seemed not to be that of a human. It was like the voice of a beast who was suffering in pain. Hearing it, their hair stood up on end with fear. “What on earth has happened? Who is inside the cave?” they puzzled.

Stepping into the cave, Mimoto yelled out, “Who are you hiding inside this deep cave? I am Mimoto of Shioda Village. Why are you moaning so loudly and painfully?”

Then Mimoto heard the faint voice of someone breathing with difficulty as if on their last gasp. “That is indeed the voice of Mimoto, isn’t it? I am the young man who comes to your house on moonlit nights. But you stuck a needle into my skin under my clothes. Why?!”

Mimoto thought she had stuck the needle into the collar of his clothes that morning but in fact it penetrated his throat accidentally. The painful breathing continued, “I am suffering in pain so badly that I cannot stand it anymore. I am the guardian spirit of this mountain and until now I could change my figure into what I wanted. But now due to this wound, my miraculous ever-changing power has been lost. I hoped to die after seeing a short glimpse of you. But if you see my original figure, you will be shocked and frightened. So, I will never see you again."

While saying this, he seemed to get weaker and weaker and Mimoto said through tears, "It is miserable for you to say such words. Whatever you look like, I won't say I am afraid of you, because you and I enjoyed each other's company every day. Please show yourself to me."

Soon terrible sounds began to be heard and a breeze with a fishy stench wafted by. At the same time the faint groan became louder. What on earth will appear from the cave? People held their breath, watching and waiting. Before long a big snake slowly slithered out from inside the cave. In fact, it was the biggest snake ever seen with a bright red tongue like fire, its big golden eyes shining like lightning. The men who followed Taifu fainted at the sight of the snake.

But Mimoto bravely and calmly covered the head of the snake gently with her jacket, then, she pulled out the needle which was stuck in the snake's neck.

Seeming to be in less pain, the serpent lifted its neck pleasantly, and quietly said to Mimoto, "I am the God of Mt. Sobo. You shall soon bear a child. The boy must grow up to be the bravest man who ever lives and who nobody can surpass. You have to bring him up with the best of care. I will

die but I will cautiously watch over your offspring's safety from now on, and they will thrive forever. Don't doubt it."

Finishing what he wanted to say, the serpent went back into the cave. At long last, his moans subsided, as he had grown weary.

Soon Mimoto gave birth to a son. He grew up to be smart and ran bare foot in wild hills and mountains. Villagers called him the chapped boy because the skin of his legs was chapped and dry even in summer. When he became an adult, he called himself Chapped Tayata and he became as brave as his father, the God of Mt. Sobo.

In the fifth generation of Tayata, a very strong samurai called Ogata no Saburou was born. He belonged to the Genji samurai family. Even Genji's opponents, the Heike samurai family, praised his fame.

The whole of Saburou's body was chapped, and he had a tail like a snake and villagers gossiped that he was an offspring of a snake, because of these strange features.

Descendants of Ogata Saburou, the family of Mitai, had power for a long time in the Takachiho region of Hyuga State. (In Japanese, the 'o' of Ogata means tail and 'gata' means figure.)

日本語訳

あかぎれ少年

祖母山は、高さ1760mの有名な山で、日向の国（現在の日本の宮崎県）と豊後の国（現在の大分県）と肥後の国（現在の熊本県）の境界にあります。

むかしむかし、この辺りに塩田の太夫という長者が住んでいました。彼には花のようなきれいな娘がいました。その娘は本当に花のようであったので、花の御本という名前でした。

彼女は成長して、結婚適齢期を迎える女性になったので、いろいろなところから、結婚の申し込みがありました。しかしこの父は娘を大変深く愛していたので、どの若者とも、娘を結婚させようとはしませんでした。

太夫は敷地内の母屋のそばに小さな家を建て、娘を一人で住まわせていました。そして娘を大切にしていたのです。

月の明るい夜になると、塩田の里に必ず横笛の音がどこからともなく聞こえてくるようになりました。

「こんなきれいな笛の音を鳴らす人は、いったい誰だろう」

村人たちは、小道に出てきて首をかしげたものでした。明るい月の光の下で、狩衣に立烏帽子をかぶった、都風の優雅な若者が静かに歩いていくのを、見たものです。

「ううーん、この里で今まであんな立派な若者は、見たことはなかった。いったいどうしたことだろう。彼はどこから来て、どこに帰っていくのだろうか」

村人たちは考え、話しこんだものでした。しかし、誰にも全く分かりませんでした。

若者は笛を吹きながら、小道を歩いていき、まもなく誰にも見られないように太夫の屋敷の門をくぐったものでした。まるで風のように、庭をこそこそと通って、決まって御本の部屋を訪れては、御本にいろんな面白い話を語ります。

そのうち、東の空が明るくなる頃、彼はどこか来たところに帰っていくのです。この立派な若者が、どこから来たのか、どこの誰なのか、御本にはさっぱり分かりません。

そのうち、御本の両親は、月の明るい夜に、あの若者が彼女の部屋に通ってきて、話をして楽しんでいることに気づきました。

母親は、御本を諭しました。「その若者がどこから来たのか、どんな人か調べなければいけません。それがはっきりするまで、あなたは彼と遊んだり、話したりしてはいけませんよ」

御本は母に答えました。

「でも、お母さん。あなたはどなたですかといつ尋ねても、彼はなにも言わないのです」

「それなら私に、良い考えがあります」とお母さんは言いました。

「縫い針と糸をまいた糸巻きをあなたにあげましょう。次に彼が来たとき、あなたは彼の着物の襟に糸のついた縫い針を突き刺しなさい。彼はその糸のついた縫い針を付けたまま帰るでしょう。あなたは、ただ糸をたどって、彼が帰る場所を突き止めればいいのです。このことを忘れてはいけません」

ある満月の夜に、若者はいつものように美しい笛の音を響かせ

ながら、御本の部屋にやってきました。御本は彼と話をしたり、遊んだりしながら、お母さんが言ったように彼に気づかれないように、彼の衣服の襟もとに縫い針を突(つ)き刺(さ)しました。明け方いつものように、あいかわらず彼はどこかへ帰っていきました。

塩田の太夫と御本は、忠実な従者たちを連れて糸をたどって、若者を捜しました。糸はどこまでも続いていました。彼らは多くの丘(おか)を登り、多くの川を渡(わた)り、多くの森を通り抜(ぬ)けて遠くまで歩いていきました。糸は彼らを、祖母山の近くまで導いていきました。ついに彼らは、祖母山の麓(ふもと)にたどり着きました。彼らは糸をたどりながら、祖母山を登り始めました。最後に、糸はこの山の中腹にある洞穴(ほらあな)の中に消えました。

「うーん、うーん」

彼らは洞穴の中で、恐ろしいうなり声がするのを聞きました。

「これはおかしい」

彼らは不思議そうに、洞穴の前で立ち止まりました。なにかがうなり声をあげていて、その音は人間のものとは思われませんでした。野獣(やじゅう)が痛みに耐(た)えかねて、声を出しているようでした。その声を聞いて、彼らの髪(かみ)の毛は恐(おそ)ろしさのあまり、総立ちになりました。

「いったい全体、なにが起こっているんだ。洞穴には誰がいるんだ」

彼らは分かりませんでした。

穴に入りながら御本は尋ねました。

「穴の奥(おく)にいるあなたは、どなたですか。私は塩田の里の御本です。なぜあなたは、激しく苦しそうに、うめき声をあげているのですか」

そして、あたかも最後のうめきのように、御本は誰かがつらさを必死に耐えているかすかな声を聴きました。

「その声は確かに、御本の声ですね。私は明るい月夜に、あなたを訪ねた若者です。しかしあなたは、私の襟の下の体に縫い針を突き刺した。なぜですか」

御本はあの朝、彼の着物の襟に縫い針を突き刺したことを、思い出しました。しかし実際には、その針は間違って彼の喉を刺したのでした。苦しそうな息づかいが続いていました。

「私はひどい痛みに苦しんでいるので、これ以上耐えることができません。私はこの山の守護霊です。いままで私は自分の姿を、思うままに変化させることができました。しかし、この傷のために、今や私の不思議な力は、その能力を失ってしまいました。私はあなたを一目見てから死にたい。しかし私の本当の姿を見たら、あなたはショックをうけて、恐れてしまうでしょう。そこで私は二度とあなたを見ません」

こう言いながら、若者は少しずつ弱くなっていくようでした。

御本は、涙をうかべて悲しそうに言いました。

「あなたがそんなことを言うと、みじめになります。あなたがどんなお姿であっても私は怖がりません。なぜなら、あなたと私は毎日一緒に遊んだ仲なのですから。どうか、あなたのお姿を私に見せてください」

まもなく恐ろしい音が聞こえ始め、魚が腐ったようなにおいの風が漂いました。同時にかすかなうなり声が、大きくなってきました。いったい全体誰が穴の中から出てくるのか。人々はかたず

をのみ、見て待っていました。

まもなくして大きな大きな蛇が穴の中からゆっくりはい出てきました。実際それは、かつてない炎のような真っ赤な舌をもった大蛇で、その黄金の目は、稲妻のように輝いていました。太夫に従ってきた従者たちは、その姿を見て意識を失いました。

しかし御本は勇敢にも、しかも落ち着いて、いとおしそうに自分の上着で蛇の頭を覆ったのです。それから彼女は、蛇の首に刺さった縫い針を引き抜きました。

痛みがなくなったようで、大蛇は嬉しそうにその首を持ち上げて、静かに御本に話しかけてきました。

「私は祖母山の神です。あなたはすぐに、子どもを産むことになります。その男の子は誰にも負けることのない、これまでにない最も勇敢な人間になるに違いありません。あなたはその子を大切に育て上げなければなりません。私は死にます、しかし今からあなたの子孫の安全を注意深く見守ります。彼らは永遠に繁栄していきます。決して疑わないように」

伝えたいことを言い終えると、大蛇は洞穴の奥に引っ込みました。しばらくして、疲れ果てたようで、大蛇のうなり声は少しずつ小さくなっていきました。

まもなく御本は、男の子を産みました。その子は賢い子に育っていき、野原や山を素足で駆けるようになりました。その子の足の皮膚は、夏でさえあかぎれができて乾いていたので、村の人々はその子をあかぎれ少年と呼びました。少年は大人になると、自分をあかぎれの大弥太と名のり、その父である祖母山の神と同じくらい勇敢でした。

大弥太の５世代後の子孫に、尾形の三郎というたいへん強い侍が生まれました。彼は源氏の侍でした。源氏と敵対していた平家の侍でさえ、彼の名声をほめたたえました。三郎の体は全体があかぎれており、蛇の尾のようなものがありました。村の人々はその変わった姿から、三郎を蛇の子孫だとうわさしました。

尾形三郎の子孫、三田井家は、日向の国の高千穂地方で長い間繁栄していました。

（なお日本語で、尾形の尾は、尻尾を意味し、形は姿を意味しています。）

Miyazaki Map

4

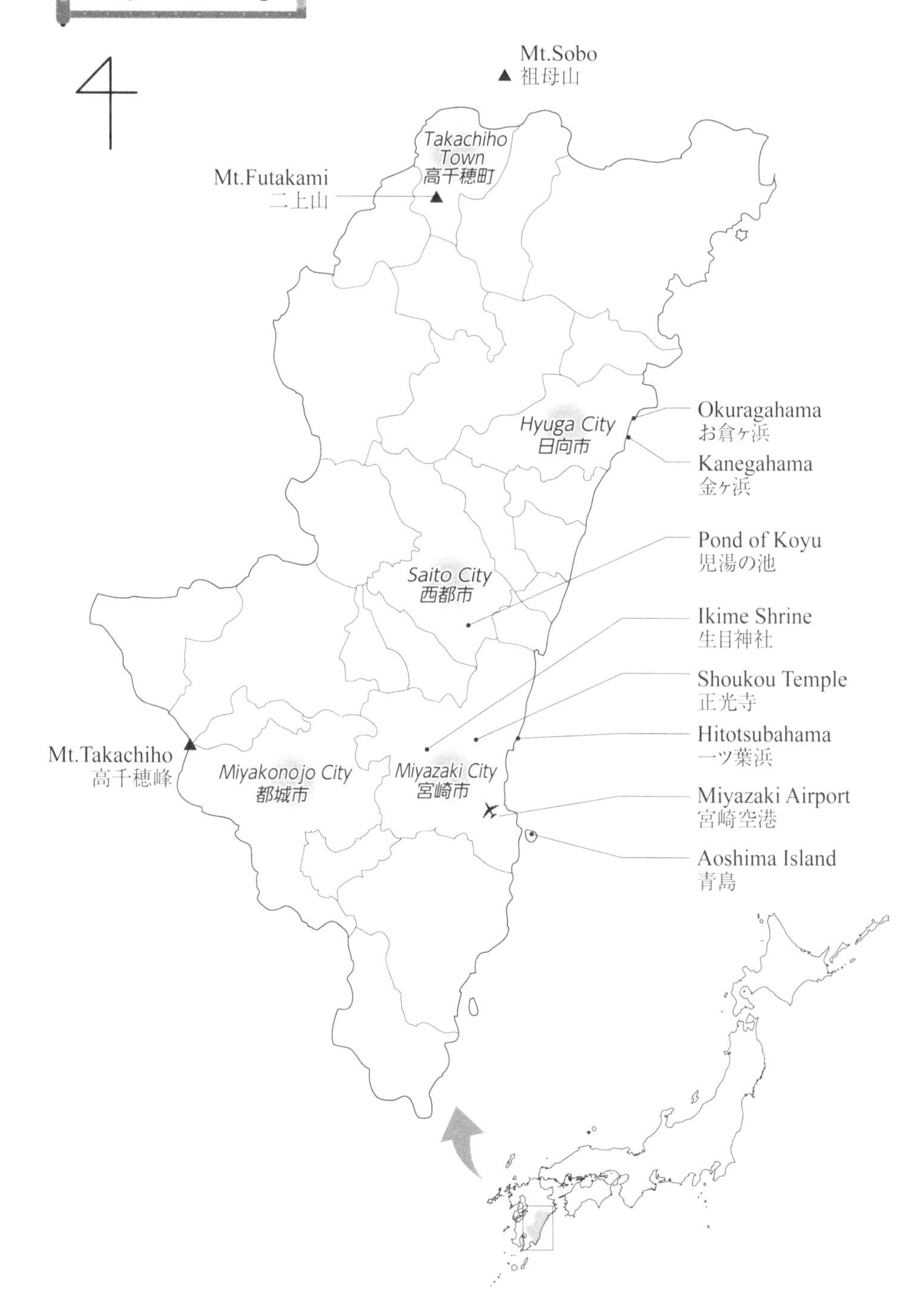

【参考文献】

作品名	著者・編者	書籍名（出版社）
ニニギノミコトと コオハナサクヤヒメ	柳　宏吉 野口逸三郎	宮崎の神話・伝説（宮崎日日新聞社）
	梅原　猛	天皇家の“ふるさと”日向をゆく（新潮社）
	次田真幸	講談社学術文庫　古事記（上）（講談社）
	宇治谷孟	講談社学術文庫　日本書紀（上）（講談社）
海幸彦と山幸彦	駒　敏郎	ふるさと伝説の旅13　南九州・海幸・山幸（小学館）
	比江島重孝	日本の民話23　日向編（未来社）
	梅原　猛	天皇家の“ふるさと”日向をゆく（新潮社）
	次田真幸	講談社学術文庫　古事記（上）（講談社）
	宇治谷孟	講談社学術文庫　日本書紀（上）（講談社）
魚籃観音	河合和己	ふるさと伝説の旅13　南九州・海幸・山幸（小学館）
	比江島重孝	日本の民話23　日向編（未来社）
お倉ヶ浜物語	比江島重孝	日本の民話23　日向編（未来社）
	日本児童文学者協会	ふるさとの民話23　宮崎県の民話（偕成社）
景清とその娘人丸	河合和己	ふるさと伝説の旅13　南九州・海幸・山幸（小学館）
	日本児童文学者協会	ふるさとの民話23（偕成社）
あかぎれ少年	中村地平	河童の遠征（鉱脈社）
	比江島重孝	日本の民話23　日向編（未来社）

おわりに

宮崎に関係する神話と民話を選びました。

宮崎で親しまれ最も宮崎らしい作品にしぼり、この6作品となりました。

英文と日本文は、相互に硬い直訳となることなく自然な文章になるよう努めました。読者は英文と日本文を参照して、宮崎の神話や民話を楽しんでいただくことができます。

英文は、作成した原文をまず、英文ネイティブ添削「英語便」所属の、英語を母語とする先生方の添削を経て、Alice Holmesさんからアドバイスをいただきました。

宮崎在住のAliceさんは、宮崎の知識があり、またナレーションを担当することから、そういう視点で入念なアドバイスをいただきました。一方、日本文には昔話などの「語り」を生かしました。

外国の読者の方のために、英文で漢字や日本の地名ならびに習慣及び文化等を説明しましたが、一方、対応した日本文を省いた部分があります。

例えば、「海幸彦と山幸彦」において、「海」「山」等の意味を、英文では解説していますが、日本文では「海」は「海」として、日本の読者には共有されていると考えて省略しました。

このほか、日本語に堪能な読者には日本の習慣や文化の解説は不要で、また物語には直接関係しないので日本文を省略したものがあります。読者は、その部分をやさしい英文で理解していただけると思います。

「プリンスニニギとプリンセスコノハナサクヤ」は、一般に「天孫降臨（てんそんこうりん）」とされている神話ですが、この神話の主人公である若い男女を表題としました。天孫降臨は、本文の中で表現しています。

次に、「海幸彦と山幸彦」において、「山幸彦がたくさんの釣り針を作った」ことを「手からこぼれるほど」と表現しましたが、日本書紀では「箕（み）からこぼれるほど」となっています。現在の読者に箕では伝わりにくいと思い、分かりやすい表現としました。

「小倉ヶ浜物語」では、お坊さんの「編（あ）み笠」は、分かりやすく「麦わらの笠つまりstraw hat」としましたが、実際は「菅（すげ）(sedge)」で編んだ笠のようですので、並列表記としました。

囲碁と将棋は対戦する２人が盤上で勝敗を争うゲームで、西洋のチェスと似ているとしましたが、ルールでは将棋の方がチェスに似ているようです。

なお、「魚籃観音」のイラストは、魚籠を手にした代表的な仏像を描いたもので、正光寺に収蔵されているものとは違う可能性があります。

企画から未経験の素人が手探りで初めたため３年かかりました。

類似の本を参考にしたり、各種類の辞書類、インターネットの翻訳やスペルチェック機能などを利用しています。

英語を母語とする複数の方が関与している英文はともかく、全体として読者の批評に耐えられるか疑問が残るところです。読者の評価次第によって、次のステップが踏み出せればよいと思います。

宮崎には興味深い神話・伝説・民話等がまだまだあります。

山幸彦及び豊玉姫と、その二人の子のウガヤフキアエズノミコトの神話、イワナガヒメのその後の伝説、高千穂の鬼八伝説、都農町の河童伝説、美郷町おせりの滝の三人姉妹のお話などが浮かびます。さらに取り組んでいきたいものです。

最後に作成に当たっては、英語を母語とする方等複数の人のご協力をいただいています。そのためこの本は、チームで作ったようなものとなりましたので、企画·編集者をイントロデュース宮崎としました。

英文の作成にご協力いただいた英語便及び所属の先生方、ことにAlice Holmes様にはあらためて感謝いたしますとともに、鉱脈社社長や担当者の小崎（おざき）美和様ほかのスタッフには、打合せや校正に対応していただきました。ありがとうございました。

イントロデュース宮崎　緒方和夫

企画・編集／イントロデュース宮崎　緒方和夫
英文アドバイス／Alice Holmes（New Zealand）宮崎在住
協力／英語便　https://www.eigobin.com
イラスト／緒方美穂
ナレーション／Alice Holmes

Planning and editing／Introduce Miyazaki　Ogata Kazuo
English Advice／Alice Holmes（New Zealand）in Miyazaki
Cooperation／Eigobin　https://www.eigobin.com
Illustration／Ogata Miho
Narration／Alice Holmes

Mythology and Folktales in Miyazaki
英語で楽しむ宮崎の神話と民話

2020年1月29日初版発行
2020年10月19日2刷発行

企画･編集　緒　方　和　夫　イントロデュース宮崎

発行者　川　口　敦　己

発行所　鉱　脈　社
〒880-8551 宮崎市田代町263番地
電話0985-25-1758

印刷・製本　有限会社 鉱 脈 社